TINY TOTS PICTURE BOOKS

MERRY MOTHER GOOSE RHYMES
by Marguerite de Angeli

LITTLE TIM AND THE BRAVE SEA CAPTAIN
by Edward Ardizzone

DINNER WITH THE GOOPS
by Gelett Burgess

WHAT IS RED?
by Suzanne Gottlieb

THINKING GAMES
by Marion Jollison

STARFISH AT THE SEASHORE
by Harriet E. Huntington

1

Marguerite de Angeli's

MERRY MOTHER GOOSE RHYMES

From BOOK OF NURSERY AND MOTHER GOOSE RHYMES. Copyright 1954
by Marguerite de Angeli. Reprinted by permission of Doubleday & Company, Inc.

Hot cross buns!
Hot cross buns!
One a penny, two a penny,
Hot cross buns!

If you have no daughters
Give them to your sons;
One a penny, two a penny,
Hot cross buns!

Sing a song of sixpence,
　A pocket full of rye;
Four and twenty blackbirds
　Baked in a pie.

When the pie was opened,
　The birds began to sing;
Was not that a dainty dish
　To set before the king?

The king was in his counting-house
　Counting out his money;
The queen was in the parlour
　Eating bread and honey.

The maid was in the garden
　Hanging out the clothes,
Along came a blackbird
　And nipped off her nose.

Simple Simon met a pieman
   Going to the fair;
Says Simple Simon to the pieman,
   "Let me taste your ware."

Says the pieman to Simple Simon,
   "Show me first your penny;"
Says Simple Simon to the pieman,
   "Indeed, I have not any."

Simple Simon went to look
   If plums grew on a thistle;
He pricked his fingers very much,
   Which made poor Simon whistle.

He went to catch a dickey-bird,
   And thought he could not fail,
Because he'd got a little salt
   To put upon its tail.

Ride a cock-horse to Banbury Cross,
To see a fine lady upon a white horse;
Rings on her fingers and bells on her toes,
And she shall have music wherever she goes.

Old woman, old woman, shall we go a-shearing?
Speak a little louder, sir, I'm very thick of hearing.
Old woman, old woman, shall I love you dearly?
Thank you, very kindly, sir, now I hear you clearly.

Jack Sprat could eat no fat,   And so between them both, you see,
His wife could eat no lean,   They licked the platter clean.

Girls and boys come out to play,
The moon doth shine as bright as day.
Leave your supper and leave your sleep,
And come with your playfellows into the street.
Come with a whoop, come with a call,

Come with a good will or not at all.
Up the ladder and down the wall,
A halfpenny roll will serve us all;
You find milk, and I'll find flour,
And we'll have a pudding in half an hour.

Hark, hark,
The dogs do bark,
The beggars are coming to town;

Some in rags,
And some in tags,
And one in a velvet gown.

Mary had a little lamb,
    Its fleece was white as snow;
And everywhere that Mary went
    The lamb was sure to go.

It followed her to school one day,
    That was against the rule;
It made the children laugh and play
    To see a lamb at school.

Little Tommy Tittlemouse   He caught fishes
Lived in a little house;   In other men's ditches.

LITTLE TIM
and the BRAVE SEA CAPTAIN

by Edward Ardizzone

Little Tim lived in a house by the sea. He wanted very much to be a sailor.

When it was fine he spent the day on the beach playing in and out of the boats, or talking to his friend the old boatman, who taught him how to make the special knots that sailors make and many other things about the sea and ships.

Sometimes Tim would astonish his parents by saying, "That's a Cunarder" or "Look at that barquentine on the port bow."

When it was wet or too cold and rough to play on the beach, Tim would visit his old friend Captain McFee.

The Captain would tell him about his voyages and sometimes give him a sip of his grog, which made Tim want to be a sailor more than ever.

But alas for Tim's hopes. When he asked his mother and father if he could be a sailor, they laughed and said he was much too young, and must wait for years and years until he was grown up. This made Tim very sad.

In fact he was so sad that he resolved, at the first opportunity, to run away to sea.

Now one day the old boatman told Tim that he was going out in his motor boat to a steamer which was anchored in the bay.

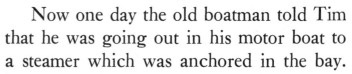

Would Tim like to come, too, and lend him a hand with the boat? Tim was overjoyed.

The boatman went on to say that the captain of the steamer was an old friend of his, and, as the steamer was about to sail, he wanted to say goodbye to him.

Tim made himself very useful, helping to stow gear into the boat, fill the petrol tank, and make all ready to go to sea.

When this was done the boatman said, "Come, give a shove, my lad," and they both pushed the boat down the shingle beach into the water, then clambered on board, and off they went.

It was a lovely day. The sea was blue, and the little waves danced and sparkled in the sunshine.

Tim got more and more excited as they neared the steamer, as he had never been in one before.

When they arrived alongside they clambered on board.

Tim was left on deck while the boatman went to see the captain, who was in his cabin.

Now Tim had a great idea. He would hide, and, when the boatman left, not seeing Tim, he would forget all about him.

This is exactly what happened.

Off went the boatman and away went the steamer with Tim on board.

When Tim thought there was no chance of being put on
shore he showed himself to a sailor.

"Oi!" said the sailor, "What are you doing out here? Come
along with me, my lad, the captain will have something to say
to you."

When the captain saw Tim he was furious and said Tim was
a stowaway and must be made to work his passage.

So they gave Tim a pail and a scrubbing brush and made

him scrub the deck, which Tim found very hard work. It made his back ache and his fingers sore. He cried quite a lot and wished he had never run away to sea.

After what seemed hours to Tim the sailor came and said he could stop work and that he had not done too badly for a lad of his size. He then took Tim to the galley where the cook gave him a mug of cocoa.

Tim felt better after the cocoa, and when the sailor found him a bunk he climbed in and was soon fast asleep. He was so tired he did not even bother to take off his clothes.

Tim soon got accustomed to life on board. As he was a bright boy and always ready to make himself useful, it was not long before he became popular with the crew. Even the captain said he was not too bad for a stowaway.

Tim's best friend was the cook, who was a family man. Tim would help him peel potatoes, wash up and tidy the galley, and in return the cook would give Tim any nice titbits that were going.

Besides helping the cook, Tim would run errands and do all sorts of odd jobs, such as taking the captain his dinner and the second mate his grog,

helping the man at the wheel,

and sewing buttons
on the sailors' trousers.

One morning the wind started to blow hard and the sea became rough, which made the steamer rock like anything.

At first Tim rather enjoyed this. It excited him to watch the big waves and see the crew hurrying about the deck making everything shipshape and secure.

But alas, Tim soon began to feel sick, and when he went down to the galley he could not eat any of the titbits that the cook gave him.

All that day it blew harder and harder and the sea became rougher and rougher till by nightfall it was blowing a terrible gale.

Poor Tim felt so sick that all he could do was to creep into his bunk and lie there, wishing he had never gone to sea.

In the middle of the night there was a terrible crash. The ship had struck a rock and lay on its side with the great waves pouring over it.

The sailors rushed on deck shouting, "We are sinking. To the boats. To the boats."

With great difficulty they launched the boats and away they went in the raging sea.

——BUT——

—they had quite forgotten Tim. He was so small and frightened that nobody had noticed him. Tim crept on to the bridge where he found the captain, who had refused to leave his ship. "Hullo, my lad," said the captain. "Come, stop crying and be a brave boy. We are bound for Davey Jones's locker and tears won't help us now."

So Tim dried his eyes and tried not to be too frightened. He felt he would not mind going anywhere with the captain, even to Davey Jones's locker. They stood hand in hand and waited for the end.

Just as they were about to sink beneath the waves Tim gave
a great cry. "We're saved. We're saved."

He had seen a lifeboat coming to rescue them.

The lifeboat came alongside and a life line was thrown to
them.

Down the life line, first Tim,
and then the captain were drawn to
safety. But only just in time.

Hardly had they left the steamer
when it sank beneath the waves.

Now followed a terrible journey through the raging sea.

The lifeboat was tossed about like a cork by the great waves which often dashed over the side and soaked them to the skin.

It was many hours before they neared land, and all were very cold and wet and tired.

When the lifeboat came into harbor the crowd, which had gathered on the quay to watch its return, gave a great cheer. They had seen Tim and the captain and had realized that the lifeboat had made a gallant rescue.

As soon as the lifeboat had moored beside the quay, Tim

was lifted out and he and the captain were taken to the nearest house.

Here they were wrapped in blankets and sat in front of the fire with their feet in tubs of hot water. Also they were given cups of hot cocoa and so were soon nice and warm, both inside and out.

Once they were warm right through they were put to bed.

They were still very tired from their terrible adventure, so they slept for hours and hours.

When they woke up the next morning, however, they both felt rested and were glad to be alive and well.

Tim hurried to send a telegram to his parents saying that he was taking the train home and that the captain was coming too.

Then he and the captain, after thanking the lifeboatmen and the kind people who had put them up, went to the station and caught their train.

On the platform they were surprised to see a large crowd waiting to see them off.

Among the crowd were many ladies who kissed Tim and gave him chocolate and fruit to eat on the journey.

Tim felt very excited and could not help feeling a bit of a hero.

But Tim became even more excited as the train neared his home town.

He had his nose glued to the window all the time looking out for familiar places and pointing them out to the captain when he saw them.

Tim's parents were at the garden gate when they arrived.
Captain McFee and the boatman were there, too.

You can imagine how pleased Tim was to see his father and
and mother and his old friends again.

The captain told Tim's parents all about their adventures

and how brave Tim had been, and he asked them if they would
let Tim come with him on his next voyage as he felt that Tim
had the makings of a fine sailor.

Tim was very pleased and happy to hear his parents say yes.

The lifeboatmen were pleased, too, as they were presented by
the Mayor with medals for bravery.

THE END

DINNER
WITH THE GOOPS

by Gelett Burgess

THE Goops they lick their fingers,
And the Goops they lick their
knives;
They spill their broth on the table-
cloth—
Oh, they lead disgusting lives!
The Goops they talk while eating,
And loud and fast they chew;
And that is why I'm glad that I
Am not a Goop—are you?

From GOOPS AND HOW TO BE THEM, published by
J. B. Lippincott Company. Illustrations redrawn.

THE Goops are gluttonous and rude,
They gug and gumble with their food;
They throw their crumbs upon the floor,
And at dessert they tease for more.
They will not eat their soup and bread
But like to gobble sweets, instead,
And this is why I oft decline,
When I am asked to stay and dine!

WHAT IS RED?

BY SUZANNE GOTTLIEB • ILLUSTRATED BY VLADIMIR BOBRI

WHAT IS RED?

RED IS THE COLOR OF MANY THINGS
—APPLES AND BERRIES AND WARM GLOWING FIRES—
THE SKY IS RED AT SUNSET AS
JONNY WALKS HOME THROUGH THE WOODS.

WHAT IS PURPLE?

SPRING FLOWERS ARE PURPLE.
SPRING RAINS FALL, AND HELP THEM GROW TOWARD THE BLUE SKY.

JONNY PICKS SOME VIOLETS
AND HURRIES UNDER A TREE TO WAIT FOR THE RAIN TO STOP.

WHAT IS BLUE?

THE SUMMER SKY IS BLUE.
IT WATCHES OVER GROWING THINGS
RIPENING TOWARD THE GOLDEN ORANGE OF HARVEST TIME.
JONNY TRAILS HIS TOES IN THE BLUE WATER OF THE BROOK
AND WATCHES THE LITTLE FISH SCURRY BY.

WHAT IS ORANGE?

AUTUMN LEAVES ARE ORANGE.
AUTUMN WINDS BLOW THEM TO THE GROUND
TO AWAIT THE WHITENESS OF FALLEN SNOW.
JONNY WALKS THROUGH THE FIELDS
WITH A GREAT ORANGE PUMPKIN JUST RIGHT FOR HALLOWE'EN.

WHAT IS WHITE?
THE SNOW IS WHITE. IT FALLS FROM THE WINTER SKIES
AND RESTS THE EARTH TILL SPRINGTIME MAKES IT BROWN AGAIN.

JONNY
STANDS AT HIS WINDOW
WATCHING THE WHITE SNOW FALL.

WHAT IS BROWN?

THE EARTH IS BROWN.
AND OUT OF ITS BROWN WARMTH
GROW GREEN THINGS.
JONNY DIGS IN THE BROWN EARTH
AND MAKES A GARDEN NEAR HIS HOUSE.

WHAT IS GREEN?

THE GRASS IS GREEN. THE TREES AND PLANTS THAT GROW
IN THE EARTH ARE GREEN, AND THE YELLOW SUN MAKES THEM SO.
THE SPROUTING PLANTS IN JONNY'S GARDEN ARE GREEN TOO.
HE WORKS HARD TO SEE THAT THEY GROW WELL.

WHAT IS YELLOW?

THE SUN IS YELLOW. ITS LIGHT MAKES THE BRIGHTNESS
OF THE DAY, AND WHEN IT SETS, THE NIGHTTIME IS BLACK.

THE YELLOW SUNLIGHT STREAMS THROUGH JONNY'S WINDOW,
TELLING HIM IT IS MORNING AND TIME TO GET UP AND PLAY.

WHAT IS BLACK?

THE NIGHT SKY IS BLACK.
ITS DARKNESS LETS US REST
AND SLEEP, TO AWAKE FOR
THE WONDERS OF A NEW DAY.

THE NIGHT IS QUIET,
AND JONNY'S BED IS WARM AND GOOD.
HE SLEEPS, AND DREAMS OF TOMORROW.

THINKING GAMES

by MARION JOLLISON

Which One Doesn't Match?

THREE GIRLS IN the top row of pictures are exactly the same, but one girl is different. Can you point to the girl who is different?

Look at the other rows. See if you can find the one picture in each row which is different from the others. Can you tell what is different about it?

Reaching Up and Bending Down

THERE ARE TIMES when we must reach up and other times when we have to bend down to do something. Look at each picture you see here and tell what you must do in each case.

Do you reach up or bend down to pick flowers?

Do you reach up or bend down to take clothes off a line?

Do you reach up or bend down to put on your shoes?

Do you reach up or bend down to dig a hole in the ground?

Matching Shapes

In EACH ROW ACROSS you will see different kinds of shapes, but only two shapes are exactly alike. Can you pick the two shapes in each row which look the same?

STARFISH AT THE SEASHORE

by Harriet E. Huntington
illustrated with photographs by the author

This is a starfish. He is called a starfish because he has five arms like a star.

A starfish is an animal. He isn't a fish at all, but he is called one because he lives in the ocean.

Although the starfish's back is made of tough skin, he cannot live long out of water. If a starfish is moist and in the shade, he might live a day. If a starfish is dry and in the sunshine, he might live only ten minutes.

Starfish are orange, green, blue, and purplish-red.

The stomach or mouth side of the starfish has hundreds of little feelers or suckers. These suckers pull the starfish whichever way he wants to go. These suckers help a starfish to turn himself over if he has fallen on his back.

Starfish are helpful because they keep the water clean. Some kinds of starfish eat old and dead sea animals. Other starfish eat mussels. A mussel is a kind of clam. When a starfish eats a mussel, he humps himself up over the mussel to pull open its shell.

You can see in the picture the suckers, feelers, and the bony
bumps which protect the starfish's skin.

The mother starfish keeps her eggs inside her body When
the eggs are ready to hatch, the mother starfish lets them go out
into the water. While the eggs are changing into starfish, they
move about in the water. When the eggs have turned into starfish, these little starfish crawl among the rocks under water.

A starfish can live to be about five or ten years old, or per-
haps older—no one really knows.

If a starfish loses an arm, he can grow a new arm. This takes about a year.

Each arm has an eye at its end. These eyes do not look like our eyes. A starfish's eyes cannot see things. They are sensitive spots which can only tell whether it is night or day.

Starfish like to move about when the tide is high. When the tide is low they hide under ledges, or in large holes in rocks.